ANCIENT GREECE
◁ MYTHS AND LEGENDS ▷

Translated by Abigail Frost

Illustrations by Jean Torton

Original by Alain Quesnel

Edited by Gilles Ragache

CHERRYTREE BOOKS

A Cherrytree Book

Adapted by A S Publishing
from *La Grèce*
published by Hachette

First published 1992
by Cherrytree Press Ltd
a subsidiary of
The Chivers Company Ltd
Windsor Bridge Road
Bath, Avon BA2 3AX

British Library Cataloguing in Publication Data
Quesnel, Alain
    Ancient Greece.—New ed.—(Myths & Legends
    Series)
    I. Title   II. Frost, Abigail
    III. Torton, Jean   IV. Ragache, Gilles
    V. Series
    292. 13

    ISBN 0-7451-5165-5

Printed in Hong Kong by Colorcraft Ltd

CONTENTS

▷ THE GREAT BATTLE ◁

High up at the summit of Mount Olympus, shielded by clouds from curious human eyes, the immortals, gods and goddesses, were enjoying a feast. Suddenly, a huge rock fell on to the table. 'Who has dared do this?' raged Zeus, king of the gods. Next, a shower of stones and flaming torches landed. Twenty-four hairy giants, with snakes for feet, loomed on top of the neighbouring mountains. These horrible creatures, the sons of the Earth, wanted to take the place of Zeus and the other gods.

Zeus's wife Hera knew what they planned. She explained that the gods could not kill the giants; only the mortal hero Heracles, Zeus's son, could do so. Even he was powerless against the giants if they used the magic powers of a mysterious plant, which grew in a secret place.

Zeus sent Athene, goddess of wisdom, to Earth to find Heracles. Then he ordered the Sun, the Dawn and the Moon to stop shining. He went to Earth and searched for the magic plant under cover of darkness. When he found it, he gathered it all up, and returned to Olympus, where Heracles had just arrived. Now the gods were ready to fight.

Heracles shot an arrow at the giants' leader. The giant fell down to Earth, but immediately got up again, seeming stronger and fiercer than before. Athene realised what had happened: 'Quick, Heracles!' she cried. 'He gets his strength from the Earth which gave him birth! Take him to a foreign country!' Heracles seized the giant, and carried him to a far-off land, where he killed him with a blow of his club.

Meanwhile, all the gods joined in the fight. Hephaistos, the smith-god, threw boiling metals at the giants. Apollo, the sun-god, shot fiery arrows. Poseidon, god of the sea, brandished his trident. Athene hurled rocks. The gods and goddesses held the giants back, but could not kill them. As each giant fell, Heracles gave him a fatal blow, in case he returned to the fray. The hero swung his club and shot his arrows without ceasing. Soon most of the giants were dead. The survivors knew they were beaten and fled, pursued all over the Earth by the victorious gods.

A giant called Enceladus, who could run faster than the others, thought he was safe, far from Greece. But Athene saw him and threw a gigantic rock at him, and knocked him into the sea. He became the island of Sicily. All the giants were defeated one by one. But not all were killed; where their bodies were buried, volcanoes rumble, showing that an angry giant still lives under the ground.

Heracles set off for new adventures, and the gods resumed their feast. They talked away as if nothing had happened; the immortals had all the time in the world.

Apollo raised his bow to shoot at the giants.

THE ANGER OF ZEUS

Lightning streaked across the sky and burnt the wicked King Lycaon's palace to ashes. Lycaon's crimes, among them human sacrifice, had angered Zeus, who changed him into a wolf. But Lycaon's sons were as bad as he. Zeus visited them, disguised as a poor traveller. Though wicked, they were hospitable, asking him to dinner. On his plate, Zeus saw human flesh. Like their father, he turned them into wolves.

Disgusted with humans, Zeus decided to drown them all in a flood. But the Titan (half god, half human) Prometheus warned his human son, Deucalion, about Zeus's plan. Prometheus loved humans, and had taught them to make fire. Deucalion and his wife Pyrrha built a ship. A tidal wave swept over all the land, except the highest mountain-tops. But Deucalion and Pyrrha were safe in their ship.

After nine days, the waters began to recede. The ship landed on the tip of Mount Parnassus. Deucalion and Pyrrha thanked Zeus for saving them and made a sacrifice in his honour. Nearby was a little temple, covered in seaweed and shells, dedicated to Themis, goddess of justice. Humbly they begged her to restore humanity to life. Zeus heard and granted their prayer. Themis told them what to do: 'Cover your heads! Take your mother's bones, and throw them behind you!'

Deucalion and Pyrrha wondered what Themis meant. They did not have the same mother! She must mean the mother of all humanity – the Earth, whose bones were stones. Quickly they gathered pebbles, and threw them over their shoulders. As they hit the ground the pebbles changed: Deucalion's became men, and Pyrrha's became women. So the couple brought humanity back to life. Their son, Hellen, grew up to be the ancestor of the Greeks, who still call themselves the Hellenes.

The great flood swept all over the land.

THE KIDNAPPING OF KORE

A carefree young girl ran over the green fields, picking flowers, not knowing someone was watching her. It was Hades, god of the dead and their world below ground. No goddess would marry this dark and sinister god. So he had set his heart on the lovely Kore, only child of the harvest-goddess Demeter. He watched her keenly as she came near, then wheeled his chariot round at full speed, seized Kore and dragged her off. The Earth roared and burst open, swallowing up the chariot. Ignoring Kore's cries for help, Hades carried her down to the dark and sorrowful kingdom of hell.

Demeter left Olympus to search the Earth for Kore. Soon she met two herdsmen, who had seen what happened. Demeter knew at once who had taken her child, and despaired. How could she beat Hades, brother of Zeus and lord of death? Crazed with grief, she roamed all over the Earth, and forbade the grasses, trees, fruits and grains to grow.

Within a few weeks the human race was starving. Men shook their fists at the sky, women wailed and children wept. Zeus heard their terrible cries of pain. He sent one god after another to soothe Demeter's rage and grief, and to ask her to make the Earth green again. The goddess refused; nothing would grow until Kore was returned to her.

At last Zeus sent Hermes to see Hades. Hermes ordered Hades to return Kore to her mother. Hades could not keep her, as she had

Sinister Hades seized Kore and dragged her off to his underground kingdom.

not eaten the food of the dead during her stay in hell. Poor Kore was too miserable and afraid to eat. Even grim Hades had to give in to Zeus's messenger. He sent for Kore and said, with a false air of kindness: 'I can see you are not happy here, and your mother is pining for you. I shall return you to her.' His words dried Kore's tears.

Hades lifted the happy Kore on to Hermes' chariot. The horses pawed the ground and the charioteer prepared to drive away. Then one of Hades' gardeners said, with a cruel grin: 'I have just seen Kore pluck a pomegranate in the orchard. She ate seven of its seeds.' The wretched girl hung her head, and admitted she had tasted just a little of the food of the dead. Hades and the gardener rode off behind Hermes and Kore to Eleusis, in eastern Greece, where Demeter was.

The goddess was overjoyed; now she could hold her lost child in her arms! Her joy was brief. Hades called his gardener to tell her about the pomegranate. Demeter collapsed in tears, crying: 'Since I shall never see my daughter again, my curse stays on the Earth. The soil will forever be sterile!'

But wise Zeus suggested an answer: for three months of the year, Kore would stay with her husband Hades. While there, she would have a new name: Persephone, which means 'bringer of destruction'. The other nine months she would spend with her mother. And so, ever since, when Kore is near her in the spring and summer, Demeter covers the Earth with green plants. When Kore's time to leave draws near, the leaves turn brown and the plants cease to grow. When Kore lives underground as Persephone, queen of hell, Demeter curses the ground and nothing grows during the three months humans call winter.

▷ KING MIDAS'S EARS ◁

Midas, king of Phrygia, was greedy for pleasure and riches. His palace stood in a beautiful garden full of fragrant roses. One evening, the gardeners found a strange creature with a man's body and goat's legs, snoring under a bush. It was a drunken satyr, sleeping off his wine. They carried him to the king. The satyr staggered upright and told Midas he was Silenus, a friend of Dionysus, the god of wine. Midas was thrilled – a chance to meet a god!

Once Silenus was sober, Midas took him to Dionysus. Glad to find his lost friend, the god offered to grant any wish the king made.

Greedy Midas did not stop to think: 'My heart's desire is for everything I touch to turn to gold.' The god smiled. 'What a foolish idea,' he thought, but true to his word, he granted Midas's wish.

Alone in his chamber, the king tried out his new power. He touched a table and jumped in surprise; the wood had turned to gold. He touched a tin cup, a bronze sword; the same thing happened. Midas grabbed everything in sight. Soon, everything in the palace, even the columns which held up the roof and the trees in the garden, was gleaming gold.

As night fell, Midas felt hungry, and called his slaves to fetch his dinner. The food looked tasty, but meat, fruit and cheese turned to gold as he touched them!

Midas called for more food, but the same thing happened. He called his courtiers to feed him, but they kept away, afraid of his terrible power. Terrified, hungry and alone, Midas saw the truth: Dionysus's gift meant death. He begged the god to deliver him from this dreadful curse. Dionysus burst into laughter when he saw what Midas's greed had done to him. But he took pity and told him to bathe in the River Pactolus. As Midas rose from the water, he touched a reed. His cursed power had gone. Since that day, tiny flakes of gold glitter in the river's sands.

After this, Midas became a follower of the forest-god Pan. Pan and the sun-god Apollo were arguing about who was the better musician. Each played a tune, Pan on his pipes, Apollo on his lyre. All except Midas agreed that Apollo had won. Midas stubbornly voted for Pan. Apollo punished Midas for his stupidity and lack of musical appreciation by giving him the ears of an ass. Midas wore a cap to hide this shameful deformity. But he had to reveal the ears to the barber who trimmed his hair and beard. He saw the barber alone, making him swear not to tell anyone what he saw.

The secret weighed on the barber's mind. He could not keep it to himself. But he had given his word, and was afraid of the king. So he dug a hole in a lonely riverbank, put his lips to it and whispered his secret to the Earth. He filled in the hole and ran away. But a reed grew on the spot and began to whisper: 'Midas has asses' ears!' The other reeds took up the tale. The whisper reached the town, and soon all the world was laughing at the king, who hid shame-faced in his palace, regretting his lack of prudence and good sense.

Even the columns that held up the palace roof turned to gold at Midas's touch.

LOOKS THAT KILL

Danae, daughter of King Acrisios of Argos, lived alone and sad in a tower of bronze, behind a tiny barred window. Her father had locked her there, after an oracle said her future son would kill him. But once Zeus took the form of a shower of gold, and slipped drop by drop through the window-bars. He made love to her and nine months later she gave birth to a son, Perseus.

Acrisios could not bear to kill his own daughter and grandson. So he put them in a wooden chest and threw it out to sea. Days later

Perseus fought the Gorgon, watching her reflection in his polished shield.

a fisherman found it washed up on the island of Sephiros. He let Danae and Perseus out and led them to the king, Polydectes.

Years passed, and Perseus grew up into a fine young man. Polydectes fell in love with Danae, and pestered her to marry him. But she preferred to live with her son. The king decided to send Perseus on a quest: to fetch the head of the Gorgon Medusa – a monster, whose hair was made of poisonous snakes. Anyone who dared to look at her was turned to stone by her gaze. Polydectes thought he was sending Perseus to certain death. But he reckoned without the gods, who hated Medusa.

Athene gave Perseus a shield polished like a mirror. Hermes gave him a sickle, a pair of winged sandals, and the dark god Hades' magic cap, which made its wearer invisible. Perseus set off well-equipped.

Medusa's land was a sinister desert. No birds sang. No living creatures moved, but all around were statues: people Medusa had turned to stone. Perseus crept up to the Gorgon, not looking directly at her, but at her reflection in Athene's polished shield. Medusa's snaky curls hissed and spat at him, but he did not turn his eyes towards her. He cut off her head with his sickle, and still without looking at it put it into a leather bag. Medusa's two sisters chased Perseus, but he put on Hades' cap and his winged sandals and escaped with ease.

Perseus went home through Ethiopia. The land there was flooded. In the waters a beautiful princess was chained to a rock, around which a sea-monster swam. Perseus learnt that Poseidon the sea-god had sent the monster, and forced the king to sacrifice his daughter Andromeda to it. Perseus offered to kill the monster if he could marry Andromeda. The king agreed. Wearing his flying sandals, Perseus leapt into the air. Invisible in his magic cap, he easily defeated the monster and freed Andromeda from her chains.

But the king did not mean to keep his promise, though Andromeda loved her rescuer. His armed men broke up the wedding ceremony. Perseus fought bravely, one against many. But he could not win with his sword alone. He shut his eyes, reached into his leather bag, and took out Medusa's head. All the soldiers were turned into stone. With Andromeda, he hastened home to Sephiros.

Polydectes was still determined to marry Danae. When the king saw Perseus alive, he teased him, saying he had not killed Medusa. 'Will you believe the evidence of your eyes?' cried Perseus, drawing the Gorgon's head from his bag and turning the cruel king and his friends to stone.

Perseus and Danae travelled to Argos, and Perseus entered the annual games. When he threw the discus, the winds blew it on to a spectator's head and killed him. Perhaps this was Zeus's will: the dead man was his grandfather Acrisios. The oracle's prophecy had come true.

THE DRAGON'S TEETH

Zeus had a weakness for mortal women, and often carried them away or made love to them. He usually took some strange shape, because otherwise his god-like form, wreathed with lightning, would kill the woman. One of them was Europa, daughter of King Agenor of Tyre. Zeus changed into a splendid white bull to carry her off to the island of Crete.

Agenor sent his five sons to search the world for their sister. Cadmus's task was to search the Greek islands. But there were so many of them! He asked Apollo's priestess at Delphi for help. Gazing into the future, she said: 'If you search for Europa, you will never find her. Look instead for a cow with the moon on each flank. Follow her and where she stops, build a city.'

Cadmus set off. Not far down the road, he saw a heifer with marks like the moon on her sides. He bought her, and let her loose. After many miles, she lay down to sleep. While Cadmus built a shrine to Athene at the spot, his men went to find water.

Nearby was a dark cave, beside a spring dedicated to Ares, god of war. Cadmus's men filled their bottles with sparkling water, not knowing a fierce dragon lived in the cave. Suddenly, it hissed and put its head outside. The men froze with fear and the dragon killed them all. When Cadmus found their bodies, he flew into a rage. He threw a huge stone at the dragon and knocked it down. Then hc killed it with his spear.

The angry hero killed the dragon with his spear.

14

As Cadmus stood admiring his kill, Athene appeared and said: 'Now is the time to plough the ground and sow the dragon's teeth!' Cadmus obeyed the goddess. As he sowed the last tooth, he looked around; the ground was bursting open and helmeted figures were rising out of it.

Soon an army was ranked over the field. Cadmus took a huge boulder and threw it among the men. They fell upon each other and began to fight to the death. Only five men were left alive at the end of the fight. They offered their services to Cadmus.

With the help of these five men, born from the Earth, Cadmus built the city of Thebes. He married Harmonia, daughter of Ares and Athene. The twelve greatest gods of Greece attended their wedding.

IN THE GREAT LABYRINTH

'O Poseidon, great god of the sea! Show me a sign of your favour!' cried Prince Minos of Crete. The waves parted and out of the sea rose a great snow-white bull, which walked, tame as a pet, over the beach to him. His two brothers bowed. The god had shown favour to Minos, and now he would be king.

Minos knew he should sacrifice the sea-god's gift; but the bull was so fine he did not want to. He found another bull from his herd and sacrificed that instead.

Deep under the sea, Poseidon raged: Minos had cheated him! He took a cruel revenge. Minos's wife gave birth to a monster, with a human body and a bull's head – the Minotaur. It could eat only human flesh.

At Minos's court there was a clever Athenian, called Daedalus, and his son Icarus. Daedalus was an inventor, a genius who could solve any problem. He soon devised a prison for the Minotaur: a maze of long winding corridors. He called it the labyrinth; once lost in it, no one could ever find his or her way out again.

Only Daedalus and Icarus knew the secret of the labyrinth. But Minos brooded; even they might tell someone. So he shut them in the labyrinth, and put guards on all the beaches, in case they should get out and sail away.

Daedalus put his imagination to work. He told Icarus to collect as many feathers as he could. Soon he had enough to build two pairs of wings. Daedalus stuck the feathers to a frame with wax. 'Now we are free of this prison; we can rise into the sky and cross the sea. But beware, Icarus; do not fly too near the sun.'

The pair went up to the roof. Icarus leant into the wind and rose up into the sky. At first he was clumsy, but rapidly his flight became graceful. Father and son flew away over the open sea. Icarus had never seen anything so beautiful as the Earth beneath him, the bright sea scattered with green islands. If only he could fly high enough to see it all! Suddenly he soared up – and at once began to fall. The sun's rays had melted the wax on his wings. He plummeted into the sea and drowned.

His father dived down. He could not save his son, but he found his body and took it to an island, now called Icare, for a proper burial. Then he flew on to Italy, where he spent the rest of his life, designing strange and beautiful buildings.

Daedalus and Icarus went to the top of the labyrinth, and flew off over the open sea.

▷ THE MINOTAUR ◁

King Aegeus of Athens was deep in sorrow. Ever since King Minos defeated him in war, he had been bound to send seven young men and seven young girls to Crete each year. Their fate was to be fed to the Minotaur that lived in King Minos's labyrinth. Sick of this waste of life, his son Theseus had decided to go as a victim, and kill the monster. Reluctantly Aegeus agreed. 'If you return safely,' he said, 'change the black sail on your ship to white. Then I will know you are safe before you land.' Theseus promised to do so, and set off for Crete.

The young Athenians arrived at Minos's palace at Knossos. Next day, they would be locked in the labyrinth, to face the Minotaur. Theseus sat up late, trying to ease their fears. Then someone came to talk to him – a beautiful young girl he had seen earlier beside Minos's throne. 'I am Ariadne, Minos's daughter. Something about you tells me you have come to kill the Minotaur. But do you realise that, even if you succeed, you will never find your way out of the labyrinth?' Theseus had never thought of this. Ariadne smiled: 'Don't worry. I will help you, if you promise to marry me and take me with you to Athens.'

Next day, Ariadne met Theseus outside the labyrinth, and gave him a spool of thread. Theseus led the others into the labyrinth. He tied Ariadne's thread to a post and unwound it along the wall as he went. Soon the young people were lost in the dark and twisting passages. They walked on tiptoe. Theseus stopped at each corner, listening for the least sound, his hand always on the hilt of his sword. All at once the Minotaur woke, bellowed and sprang at the young hero. But Theseus was ready, and killed the creature with a single thrust.

Theseus followed his thread over the route he had taken. Soon he was by Ariadne's side. Quickly the Athenians stove in the sides of the nearest Cretan ships. Then they all climbed aboard the ship they had come in.

Minos sent his few ships that were still seaworthy out to stop the Athenians, but, under cover of darkness, they escaped. Some days later, they reached the isle of Naxos, and landed there to collect fresh food. Theseus thought only of the glory awaiting him in Athens. He imagined himself heading a triumphal procession, the hero of the crowd. He was so eager to get home, he forgot Ariadne and set sail while she was sleeping on the beach. When she woke, she saw the ship far away on the horizon. But the god Dionysus passed by and saved her.

Meanwhile, Theseus was sailing within sight of Athens. Still caught up in dreams of glory, he forgot his promise to Aegeus, to change the black sails for white.

Since his son's departure, the old king had spent all his time on the Acropolis, gazing at the waves, in search of his son's white sail. But when the sail appeared, it was black. 'Theseus is dead,' he cried and threw himself into the sea – which is now called the Aegean in his honour.

Theseus glowed with happiness as he walked on shore. His smile faded when he learnt the sad news. His carelessness had killed his father.

But Theseus dried his tears and set about being a good king. Under his wise rule, Greece knew peace and Athens prosperity.

The Minotaur bellowed and bounded out at Theseus.

▷ PYGMALION'S WIFE ◁

The sculptor Pygmalion could not settle to his work. His life seemed empty and purposeless, always alone in his studio. He longed to be married, but did not care for any of the women he met. His heart was in thrall to Aphrodite, goddess of beauty and love. He thought of nobody but her.

In his despair, Pygmalion had an idea. After all, he was a famous artist. For the first time in ages, he smiled a little. He went to the market to order the finest, whitest, most gleaming ivory he could find. Back at his studio, he busied himself preparing his tools, which had been idle so long. At last the ivory arrived. His chisel would make this dead stuff into the most beautiful statue of Aphrodite there had ever been. He stroked the ivory gently and set to work. Night and day, without stopping to eat or sleep, Pygmalion carved away.

One evening Pygmalion stopped work. Before him, surrounded by ivory shavings, stood a woman of matchless beauty. Pygmalion fell in love with his own creation. But he knew the truth: Galatea, as he called her, was only dead

matter. She had no sense or feelings. Pygmalion prayed to Aphrodite to take pity on him. Then he went to bed. As he slept, Aphrodite entered. Her power changed Galatea from a statue to a living woman. The cold, hard ivory melted into soft warm flesh. Life sparkled in Galatea's eyes.

Suddenly the sleeping Pygmalion felt a gentle touch on his face. Without opening his eyes, he brushed it away. Then he cried out: Galatea was there, alive! Aphrodite had answered his prayer and brought him a wife.

As Pygmalion slept, Aphrodite changed the statue into a living woman.

▷ ATALANTA ◁

King Iasus of Arcadia longed for an heir to his kingdom. He had no son and his daughter had a rebellious nature. She cared only for hunting and athletics, and wanted never to marry. Iasus insisted she find a husband, to rule after him. She agreed, on one condition: 'I will marry whoever can beat me in a race; but all who fail must die.'

Many princes tried the test, but Atalanta easily beat them all. Then Prince Melanion presented himself to the king. This fearless prince had begged Aphrodite's aid. She gave him three golden apples, because she did not approve of girls who rejected love.

Atalanta and Melanion started their race neck and neck. Then Melanion dropped a golden apple. Atalanta saw it gleaming on the track and stopped to pick it up, but soon regained the ground she had lost. Melanion dropped his second apple; Atalanta again slowed down to take it, then put on speed to catch up. But when Melanion dropped the last apple, the delay was fatal – he passed the winning-post. Gracefully, Atalanta accepted defeat, and the pair were married next day.

Atalanta slowed down when she saw the golden apple.

THE TWELVE OLYMPIANS

Hades

Poseidon

Ares

Athene

Aphrodite

The Greeks worshipped many gods. Greek gods were not perfect. They had faults, just like humans. They could be greedy, proud or lustful, and they often quarrelled among themselves. The Greeks feared them as much as they loved them; if a mortal angered a god, even over a little thing, he was probably doomed.

The twelve main gods were called the Olympians, because they were thought to live on top of Mount Olympus, the highest mountain in Greece. They kept themselves immortal by eating special food, called ambrosia, and a special drink, called nectar.

The Greek gods can often be recognised in art by their clothes, or by an animal or object which is their symbol. In the legends, they often appeared to mortals in disguise; Zeus, for example, in his true form, was surrounded by burning light, which would kill any mortal who came close to him. They could easily change their shapes, into animals, humans or even a shower of gold, the guise in which Zeus visited Danae.

Zeus, the wise king of the gods, was also the god of thunder and lightning. He was usually pictured as a severe old man with a thick beard. His symbol was an eagle, king of the birds. He could kill a mortal who displeased him instantly with a thunderbolt or a flash of lightning from the sky.

Greek gods in Rome
The Romans worshipped the Greek gods, but used mostly their own Latin names for them. They are:

   Zeus: Jupiter
   Poseidon: Neptune
   Hades: Pluto
   Hera: Juno
   Ares: Mars
   Athene: Minerva
   Artemis: Diana
   Aphrodite: Venus
   Hermes: Mercury
   Dionysus: Bacchus
   Demeter: Ceres

Because Latin was the language used by scientists in the Middle Ages and the Renaissance, all the planets in the Solar System (except Earth) have the Latin names of Greek gods.

Dionysus

Hephaistos

Hermes

Hera

Zeus

Apollo

Artemis

Zeus's wife, Hera, was goddess of marriage. Mortal women who attracted Zeus also attracted her jealousy. Her symbol was the peacock, the bird with watchful eyes in the feathers of its tail.

Zeus ruled the earth and the sky; his brothers had their own kingdoms. Poseidon, shown carrying a trident (a fisherman's three-pointed spear) was the ruler of the sea. The Underworld, land of the dead, was the kingdom of Zeus's other brother, Hades.

The other Olympians were Zeus's sons and daughters. Ares, the god of war, was always shown dressed in armour, ready to fight. He brought trouble and discord to Olympus; though the Greeks were often great warriors, they always preferred peace.

His sister Athene, goddess of wisdom, was also shown dressed in armour. She ruled over the sciences, and gave humans many useful inventions. She was the special protector of the city of Athens, and her symbol was an owl.

Aphrodite was the goddess of love. She was born from the foam of the sea. Though she was married to the lame smith-god, Hephaistos, she really loved Ares. Her symbol was a pair of doves.

Another brother and sister were Artemis, the moon-goddess, and Apollo, god of the sun. Artemis lived unmarried in the forest, with a band of maidens who followed her in the hunt. Apollo was the patron god of music, poetry and art, and played the lyre beautifully.

Apollo ruled the spiritual side of humanity; his opposite was Dionysus, god of wine. Dressed in a leopard's skin and crowned with vine-leaves, he brought laughter and jollity with him. But he had his sinister side: sometimes his followers became mad and bloodthirsty.

When the gods wanted to send messages to humans, they often sent Hermes as a go-between. He had wings on his helmet and sandals to help him fly between Olympus and Earth. His symbol was a caduceus, a rod with snakes twined around it; he protected merchants, doctors – and also thieves!

Heracles grasped the lion's neck and squeezed. The beast's struggles were useless.

▷ THE LION'S SKIN ◁

A terrible roar echoed through the forests. The monstrous lion had taken another victim. The shepherd Molorchos thought sadly of his son, killed by the monster. Around the town of Nemea, neither flocks nor men were safe.

Suddenly Molorchos saw a huge figure in the doorway. 'I am Heracles,' thundered the newcomer. 'Can I stay here for while, before I kill the lion?' Astonished, Molorchos stammered: 'Of course!' He could not believe a human, however strong, would dare fight the lion. But Heracles was no ordinary mortal: his father was the god Zeus.

The goddess Hera, who hated Heracles, had made him a slave of King Eurystheus of Argos, the most cowardly king in Greece. The very sight of his slave's muscles made the king shake with fear. To get Heracles out of his sight, he ordered him to perform twelve labours – unbelievably dangerous tasks. Killing the Nemean lion was the first.

As Heracles left, he told Molorchos to wait thirty days. 'If I return victorious, we must sacrifice a ram to Zeus; if not, please make the sacrifice in my honour.'

Heracles reached Nemea at noon. The streets were deserted, the houses empty; all the people had been eaten by the lion or had fled. He crept quietly into the forest, following the beast's footprints. Suddenly he heard a rustle in the bushes. The huge lion growled and padded out. Heracles drew his bow and shot a volley of arrows. But they bounced off the lion's thick skin and broke, troubling it no more than insect bites. The lion's skin bent his sword, so he tried hitting its head with his heavy club. The club broke under its own force. The lion shuddered; the blow had made its ears ring. Heracles dropped his useless weapons, and chased the lion to its den.

The lion had no chance to blink an eye before Heracles leapt on its back. He grasped its neck and squeezed. The beast's struggles were useless. Heracles strangled it in his strong arms. He lifted its body on his shoulders and strode away.

Thirty days had passed when he reached Molorchos's house. The shepherd was overjoyed to see Heracles alive and victorious. The pair sacrificed a ram to Zeus, then Heracles cut himself a new club, and set off for Argos. Eurystheus screamed when he saw the lion's body.

Heracles wanted to keep the lion's skin, but it was too tough to cut. Inspired by the gods, he tore off one of the creature's own claws to do the job. They were sharper than the best steel. From that time, Heracles always wore the Nemean lion's skin.

THE HYDRA AND THE SHY DEER

Heracles' next labour was to kill the Hydra, which terrorised the marshes of Lerna. His nephew Iolaos came with him. The Hydra had the body of a dog, and nine heads like hideous serpents; its breath and blood were deadly poison. The middle head was immortal. Heracles attacked the monster with his heavy club – but as he crushed one head, two or three more grew in its place. Heracles thought quickly, and told Iolaos to sear each bleeding neck with a

burning torch as he knocked the head off. Soon only the immortal head was left. Heracles struck it off with his sword. It lay on the ground and hissed. Heracles buried it under a huge rock. He dipped some arrows in the Hydra's poisoned blood. Now the slightest scratch from them would kill.

King Eurystheus now had another hard task for his slave: 'Bring me the hind of Ceryneia.' This beautiful, shy deer was not dangerous, but almost impossible to catch. She had golden horns and hooves of brass, and could run farther and faster than any living creature. Heracles tracked the hind for a year, through the mountains and forests, and up into the icy, fog-bound lands beyond the North Wind. Whenever he caught a glimpse of her, the deer shied away. However fast he ran, he could not catch her up. Sometimes she stopped far away, and looked back, seeming to tease him. As soon

as he moved, she darted off again. He never gave up the chase, and at last, she stopped to drink at a river. Heracles hesitated; he did not want to hurt the lovely creature. Carefully he aimed his bow at her leg. His arrow slipped exactly between the tendon and the bone, and drove into the ground. She was trapped, without losing a drop of blood.

Heracles carefully removed the arrow and lifted the deer onto his shoulder. Then Artemis, appeared, enraged. 'This deer is sacred to me! You have no right to take her!' Heracles explained that he had no choice, because he was bound to Eurystheus. He had not meant to affront Artemis. She let him go on his way, providing he promised to free the deer after his master had seen her. Heracles kept his word. But he was not free of Eurystheus, who had more work for him.

However fast Heracles ran, he could not catch the beautiful deer.

▷ THE AMAZON QUEEN ◁

Now Heracles' master sent him on more expeditions. He had to capture a monstrous boar in the land of Erymanthus. Then he had to clean the stinking stables of King Augeas, which had not been cleaned for thirty years. He did it by diverting two rivers. At Lake Stymphalus, he scared away a flock of vicious, man-eating birds with a magic rattle. Then he sailed to Crete to capture a fire-breathing bull. Next, he tamed wicked King Diomedes' war-horses, which fed on human flesh.

The next labour meant a voyage to the Black Sea. Heracles had to bring Eurystheus a jewelled girdle that the war-god Ares had given to Hippolyta, queen of the Amazons. Heracles knew no fear, but what he had heard of the Amazons worried him. They were ferocious women warriors. According to those few who had seen them and lived to tell the tale, they hated men, and killed all their male children. It was said, too, that they cut off their right breasts to help them draw their bows. Just to be on the safe side, Heracles took a company of warriors with him.

Heracles' ship dropped anchor at a pleasant harbour. On the hills above, he saw the Amazon cavalry guarding the city. The Amazons drew their swords, gave a war-cry, and galloped down to the harbour, their long hair streaming behind them. Hippolyta was easy to recognise by her splendid armour.

Instead of challenging Heracles to fight, Hippolyta hushed her warriors and welcomed him. He invited her on to his ship, leaving guards outside. As they talked, Hippolyta began to feel strangely tender towards the handsome hero. When he told her about his quest, she unlinked her girdle's golden buckle and gave it to him. Heracles took the gift gratefully, glad to have performed the labour without fighting.

This easy victory displeased Hera. She took the shape of an Amazon and went among the warrior-women spreading the rumour that Heracles had come to kidnap their queen and sell her as a slave. The angry Amazons put on their armour, took up their weapons and attacked Heracles' guards. Heracles heard the noise and went on deck; the Amazons were beating his men!

Heracles suspected treason, but he kept his wits about him. He captured Hippolyta's sister, and threatened to kill her unless he was allowed to leave safely with the girdle. The Amazon queen called her troops off, and Heracles and his party left. Eurystheus took the girdle and hung it in Hera's temple as an offering.

But the foolish king was still not satisfied. Next, he sent Heracles to capture a magic herd of cattle from the ogre Geryon, who had three heads and six arms. Heracles took the herd, but Geryon chased him along the coast of North Africa, then joined to Europe at the end of the Mediterranean Sea. Heracles pushed the two continents apart at the place now called the Straits of Gibraltar; the ancients called it the Pillars of Heracles. Next, he had to fetch three golden apples from the garden of the Hesperides, sisters whose job was to guard them. Heracles killed a dragon set to watch over the tree on which the apples hung. Then Eurystheus sent Heracles down to hell to capture Cerberus, the monstrous three-headed dog that guarded Hades' sinister kingdom. Eurystheus was so frightened when he saw Cerberus, he hid in a huge brass jar.

At last Heracles had finished his twelve labours, and he was free again.

The angry Amazons fought to rescue their queen.

▷ HELEN OF TROY ◁

Helen, daughter of King Tyndarus of Sparta, was the most beautiful woman in the world. Kings and princes flocked to Sparta, hoping to win her hand. Tyndarus was afraid to choose any of them, knowing the jealousy that would result. One of the suitors had been Odysseus, King of Ithaca. But seeing he had no chance, he decided to marry another princess, Penelope, instead. Tyndarus asked him for help. 'Let Helen make the choice,' said Odysseus, 'But first, make all her suitors swear to defend her husband, come what may.'

The suitors gathered to swear the oath in Tyndarus's great hall. Helen entered to make her choice. She placed a coronet of flowers on the man's head. Her father smiled, and announced that he would give his throne to the man she had chosen, Menelaus.

Far away, on Mount Ida, lived a young shepherd, Paris, who was famous for his judgement. Hermes, the gods' messenger, came to him one day to ask his help.

All the gods and goddesses, except one, had been at a wedding feast. Eris, goddess of discord, had not been invited, because she always provoked quarrels. She decided to spoil the feast. As the gods and goddesses chattered, she threw a golden apple among them. Carved on it were the words, 'to the fairest'. At once, Hera, Athene and Aphrodite began to argue about who should have it. Zeus dared not choose between them, and sent Hermes to find a mortal to judge.

He asked Paris to choose but Paris was unable to make up his mind. The goddesses, seeing this, tried to sway his mind with gifts. Hera offered power and wealth; Athene wisdom and knowledge. Aphrodite promised him the most beautiful woman in the world for his

Paris found it hard to choose which goddess should win the apple.

wife. Paris gave the apple to her, and Hera and Athene hated him for ever after.

Aphrodite then told Paris a secret. He had not been born a shepherd-boy. His real parents were Priam and Hecuba, king and queen of Troy, the greatest city of Asia Minor. Before he was born, Hecuba dreamed she was giving birth to a flaming torch that burnt down the palace. The soothsayers said this meant that her child would be the destruction of Troy. So Priam left the baby on the slopes of Mount Ida, where a shepherd found him and brought him up as his own son.

Paris decided to find his real parents. He went to Troy, where he won the annual games. When Priam handed him the crown, Paris gave him the cloth he had been wrapped in as a baby. Forgetting the prophecy, Priam and Hecuba welcomed their son home.

Later, Priam sent Paris on business to Sparta. Menelaus was abroad, and Helen welcomed Paris in his stead. Paris realised she was the wife Aphrodite had promised him. Helen fell in love with him, and willingly sailed to Troy in his ship. When Menelaus returned, he angrily declared war on Troy.

THE MADNESS OF ODYSSEUS

Odysseus, King of Ithaca, frowned anxiously. A fleet of ships was sailing towards his peaceful island. Why were they coming? Cunning Odysseus knew the answer: they had come to take him and his men to war. Odysseus and his wife Penelope had a baby son called Telemachus. Ithaca was a happy and prosperous island, and Odysseus did not want to leave it to fight – and perhaps die – in far-away Troy. Quickly he made a plan.

The Greek kings, Agamemnon, Menelaus and Palamedes greeted Penelope, and asked where her husband was. 'Alas,' she said, 'Odysseus has lost his reason. Come to the beach and see for yourselves. He is not fit to fight with you.' At the beach, the kings saw an extraordinary sight. Odysseus, half-naked, was ploughing the sand. Yoked to the plough were an ox and an ass. Strangest of all, Odysseus was sowing the furrow – with salt, not seed! 'He's insane!' said Agamemnon. Palamedes was more sceptical. 'Just look,' he said, and snatched baby Telemachus from his mother's arms. Then he laid him on the sand in the animals' path. They would surely trample him to death.

But Odysseus halted the animals, and admitted he was not mad after all. He kissed his weeping wife, fetched his armour and told his men to do the same. They all trooped down to the shore, and sailed off with the others. Sadly he looked back at his home, praying to return some day.

When the Greek fleet was assembled, it was the greatest armed force ever seen. All the Greek kings were there, with their most valiant warriors. Agamemnon inspected them with pride, but one person was missing. Where was Achilles, the greatest of them all? Nobody knew for sure, but rumour said that his mother, the sea-nymph Thetis, had disguised him as a girl by magic and made him forget that he was a great warrior. Now he lived in the women's quarters of King Lycomedes' palace, spending his days weaving tapestries and dancing. Odysseus, after leaving home against his will, did not see why Achilles should get away with it.

An old pedlar knocked at Lycomedes' palace gate, with a basket full of jewels, silks and ribbons. The young princesses welcomed him in, and tried on all his wares with cries of joy. Achilles did just the same. Right at the bottom of the basket, he found a fine sword, a shield and a lance. He looked stunned, then cried: 'These are what I want!' His memory came flooding back. The pedlar was Odysseus in disguise. He took Achilles from the palace. They summoned Achilles' warriors, the Myrmidons, and his cousin Patroclus, and all set off together.

The Greek army, a hundred thousand strong, was ready to go. The sails were set, but the ships did not move. The soothsayer Calchas explained that the fleet could not leave because Agamemnon had offended Artemis. He must sacrifice his daughter, Iphigenia, to appease her. All the hardened soldiers wept as their general raised his knife. But at the last moment, Artemis put a stag in Iphigenia's place, and took her to join her hunting-band. The winds blew up, and at last the Greeks set sail.

Palamedes laid baby Telemachus down in the animals' path.

ACHILLES' HEEL

Every evening, the Greek troops struggled miserably back to camp. Some helped their wounded comrades; others carried the bodies of the dead. All were exhausted. The siege of Troy had gone on for years. Every day, the Greeks attacked, and every day, many died. But they never breached the city walls. Hector, Priam's son, always held them back. His courage and strength seemed superhuman. Only Achilles could beat him; but he was sulking in his tent, refusing to fight, after a bitter quarrel with Agamemnon about a slave-girl. He seemed not to care about the war.

One night, as funeral pyres lit up the sky, Achilles' cousin Patroclus spoke to him. 'I cannot bear to see our friends suffer and die for nothing. If you will not face the Trojans, give me your armour and chariot. Hector will think I am you.' Achilles hesitated, but at last agreed.

The sun rose to a clatter of chariots and weapons, as the Greeks prepared for battle. Suddenly the camp fell silent. Achilles' Myrmidons had come to fight, for the first time since the siege began, Patroclus (whom everyone took for Achilles) at their head. The Greeks all cheered and attacked with renewed courage. The Trojans stood on the city walls as usual. But their confidence faltered when they saw a new figure among the Greek forces. Surely it was Achilles!

Even Hector felt a moment's fear. Then he challenged the man to single combat. Patroclus,

34

worthy of his friend, fought fiercely. But the god Apollo, who favoured Hector, joined the battle, invisible to the mortal soldiers, and brought Patroclus down. Hector killed him; but, to his dismay, when he took Achilles' armour and helmet – his right as victor – he found he had killed someone else.

Now Achilles thought only of avenging Patroclus. His mother Thetis gave him new armour, made by Hephaistos. He was ready to take on Hector. His Myrmidons advanced, cutting hundreds down; the Trojan defenders shook in panic and terror. But Hector stayed calm; Troy's fate was in his hands. He stood firm as the angry Achilles attacked.

Then Apollo came to help. He turned Hector into a column of mist, to confuse Achilles. But Achilles spotted him at last, leaped from his chariot and chased him round the city walls. At the gate Hector saw his brother, Deiphobus, who chided him: 'Have you no shame, Hector? You're Troy's only hope! Fight!' Hector turned back to face Achilles. But it was not his brother who spoke; it was the Greeks' friend Athene, in disguise. Hector had no time to save himself from Achilles' sword.

The Trojans were in disarray. Achilles seemed invincible; arrows or swords could not wound him. But Apollo told Paris he had a secret weakness. When Achilles was a baby, his mother had bathed him in the River Styx, which flowed through Hades' kingdom. The water of death made his skin impossible to wound. But he could be wounded on his heel, where Thetis had held him. Paris shot a poisoned arrow at Achilles' weak spot; and so the Greeks lost their greatest hero.

Despite Apollo's help, Achilles spotted Hector at last.

▷ THE TROJAN HORSE ◁

Another terrible day's fighting was over. The Greeks returned to their tents, the Trojans to their houses. With Achilles and Hector dead, the war had reached a stalemate. In the Greek camp, bitter voices were raised: 'Ten years' fighting, thousands dead or maimed! All for a woman!' Some were for sailing home. But Odysseus had a better idea. If the war could not be won by force, perhaps it could be won by cunning. He went to Agamemnon and told him a secret plan.

Some nights later, Trojan sentries captured a Greek soldier at the city gate. His hands were in fetters. They took him and locked him up for the night.

Next morning, the defenders on the walls could not believe their eyes. All the Greek tents and ships had gone. In their place was a huge wooden horse. King Priam was told about it while he was seeing the sentries and their captive, Sinon. Perhaps he could explain.

Sinon said that the Greeks had gone home, sick of the never-ending war. Calchas had told Agamemnon to sacrifice a man to assure favourable winds. Sinon had been chosen, but had escaped in the confusion of striking camp. The horse was an offering to Athene; if the Trojans ignored it, she would remain their enemy, but if they took it into the city she would take their side in future.

The Trojans discussed what to do. Priam's daughter, the prophetess Cassandra, said they should leave the horse alone: disaster and destruction would follow it into the city. An old priest called Laocoon agreed with her: 'Fear the Greeks, even if they bring gifts.' But Priam brushed their warnings aside. A troop of soldiers dragged the horse within the walls of Troy.

Night fell again, and the people of Troy went to bed, glad to be at peace. But as they slept, a trapdoor opened in the wooden horse's body. A rope fell out, and one by one, a dozen soldiers climbed down into the streets of Troy. This was Odysseus's plan: the Greek ships had only sailed a little way away, and now the army was waiting for the gates of Troy to be opened.

Sinon lit a beacon on Achilles' tomb – the sign for the invasion. The Greeks poured into the city and set it on fire. Only a few Trojans escaped the fury of the Greeks. One of them, Prince Aeneas, escaped with a few men, carrying his old father on his back and leading his little son by the hand. They sailed away, and after many adventures, landed in Italy. The Romans said that Aeneas was an ancestor of their emperors.

In a corner of the city, Menelaus found Helen, shaking with fear. He had meant to kill her, but when he saw her, he could not bear to. She followed him to his ship, without a thought for Paris. The former shepherd-boy was dead, having fought to the last to save the city which the oracle had foretold he would bring to destruction.

As the Trojans slept, a dozen soldiers crept from the horse into the city's streets.

IN THE CYCLOPS' CAVE

'Land!' cried a sailor, and Odysseus's crew cheered. Stormy seas and rocky shores had driven them off-course. For weeks they had been sailing without rest. Now they saw a group of green islands ahead. They hauled the ship up on a beach and settled down to sleep. But Odysseus wanted fresh provisions; he took a dozen men in a boat to the biggest island, with two skins of wine to drink. The island was pleasant and fertile. As they explored, they found a huge cave, half-hidden by laurel trees. Around it grazed goats; they caught one and built a fire to roast it. Inside the cave were neat piles of cheeses; they entered to take some. Then a Cyclops – a giant with one eye in the middle of his head – drove a flock of sheep into the cave. He rolled a huge stone over the entrance. When he saw his visitors, he roared: 'What are you doing in my cave?' Odysseus said that they were Greeks returning from the Trojan War, and asked for hospitality in the name of the gods. The giant grunted. Then he bent down and picked up two men, raised them to his mouth and crunched them up. Afterwards he lay down and went to sleep.

Odysseus shook with rage and frustration. Only the giant was big enough to remove the stone over the cave's entrance, so he could not kill him. How could they escape?

Next morning, the Cyclops had two more men for breakfast. Then he rolled the stone from the entrance, led his sheep out and rolled it back again. Odysseus seized an olive branch from the ground, whittled it to a point and hardened it in the giant's fire. Then he hid it in a crack in the rock.

At sunset, the giant returned with his sheep, and chose two more Greeks for supper. When he had finished, Odysseus approached politely and offered him a skin of the wine he had brought with him. The Cyclops swallowed it all. Odysseus gave him the second skin. 'Who should I thank for thish delicioush drink?' asked the fuddled Cyclops. 'My name is Nobody,' said cunning Odysseus. 'Well, Nobody, you're my friend. I'll have you for breakfast tomorrow.'

The giant had never drunk wine before, and quickly fell asleep. Odysseus and his men took the olive-branch from its hiding-place, and heated it in the fire's embers. Then they plunged it into the Cyclops' single eye. His howls of pain woke all the other Cyclopes on the island. 'Who has hurt you, Polyphemus?' they asked. 'Nobody has done this!' he replied. The others went away, thinking their friend was crazy.

Polyphemus closed up his cave for the night, hoping to take revenge next morning. But he had to let his sheep out first. He counted them out by feeling each one's back. He did not know, blind as he was, that Odysseus had disguised himself and his men under sheep-skins. So they all escaped.

Once outside, they stood up and ran for their boat. The sailors rowed quickly away, while Odysseus stood up, shouting mockingly to Polyphemus: 'Nobody blinded you – Nobody but Odysseus, King of Ithaca!'

Odysseus did not know Polyphemus was a son of Poseidon, the sea-god. The Cyclops called on his father to avenge him. Then he grabbed a huge rock and threw it towards Odysseus's voice. It landed harmlessly in the sea, and made a great wave, which carried the little boat back to the main ship. But now Odysseus had to make the long voyage home with the sea-god as his enemy.

The blind giant counted his sheep – and Odysseus's men – by feeling their backs.

▷ ODYSSEUS'S WANDERINGS ◁

Poseidon was angry. Odysseus kept escaping the storms he sent. He still had every one of the twelve ships he started with. Now he was begging Aeolus, god of winds, for help. Aeolus gave him a huge leather bag, tied fast with cord. As a result they had fairer weather, and for ten days sailed on course for Ithaca. But one night, as Odysseus slept, his inquisitive crew untied the bag. A tempest blew up: Aeolus had put all the winds except the West Wind, which blew towards Ithaca, into the bag, and the foolish sailors had let them all out at once.

The winds carried the ship to an island with a fine harbour. Eleven ships stopped, but Odysseus made his men sail on. Next day the islanders – cannibals – killed and ate all the other crews.

The next island was Aeaea. Odysseus sent a few men to look around. Only one returned. He said they had met wild beasts that had tried to make friends. Then the island's queen, Circe, asked them to dinner. All but Odysseus accepted. He watched as his friends ate their food and turned at once into pigs.

Odysseus asked the gods for help. Hermes brought him a herb called moly to undo Circe's magic. He went to Circe's palace, and ate her food. To her surprise he kept his own shape.

Realising this man was favoured by the gods, she turned his crew back into men. He asked her the way back to Ithaca. 'Only the prophet Tiresias knows, and he is dead,' she said. 'But I can make a spell to send you to Hades' kingdom to ask him.' Odysseus made the journey, spoke to Tiresias and returned safely.

As Odysseus set off, Circe warned him of the Sirens. These creatures lived on a rock. They had the bodies of birds and the faces of beautiful women. They lured sailors to their deaths with haunting songs. Odysseus wanted to hear the songs, but also to stay alive. So he blocked his sailors' ears with wax, and made them tie him to the mast. As they sailed past, he screamed to be set free, but the sailors, hearing nothing, kept the ship on course.

Now they met another danger: the sea-monsters Scylla and Charybdis. Charybdis made a whirlpool by gulping and spitting out huge quantities of water. If you escaped her whirlpool, you went too near Scylla who had six heads ready to snatch sailors. But Odysseus managed to sail just between the two hazards.

Next they reached the sun-god Hyperion's island. The hungry men butchered and ate some of his sacred cattle, though Odysseus refused to join their feast. To punish this crime, a great wave broke the ship on a rock. All aboard were drowned, except Odysseus, who clung to a spar, and drifted to an island where a nymph called Calypso lived. She tended him kindly, and he lived with her for years, forgetting his home and Penelope. But at home, Penelope was in trouble. Zeus told Calypso to let Odysseus build a boat and go.

The foolish sailors released a tempest which buffeted their ship to and fro.

ODYSSEUS RETURNS

Ithaca was in disorder. Hundreds of princes, thinking Odysseus dead, had come to pay court to Penelope, all hoping to gain the throne. They lived at her expense in the palace, pressing her to choose a husband. They were greedy and rough, and her son, Telemachus, though grown to manhood, could not control them. Penelope knew in her heart Odysseus was alive. She told the suitors she would choose one of them when she had finished the tapestry she was weaving. But every night, alone in her quarters, she unravelled the day's work.

Athene decided something should be done. She appeared to Telemachus, and told him to go and ask the other Greek kings what had happened to his father. Then Zeus, at her request, made Calypso set Odysseus free.

Poseidon sent a last storm to wreck Odysseus, but once again, he was washed up on a strange shore and saved. A princess called Nausicaa found him and took him to her father, the king. Odysseus told them all his adventures: ten years at war, and ten on the stormy seas. Now he could go home.

Nausicaa's father gave Odysseus a ship. When it reached Ithaca, he was fast asleep. The kindly crew left him sleeping under a shady olive tree. When he awoke he wondered where he was. Then Athene appeared to him. She disguised him as an old beggar, saying he was in danger in his own land. He must find his old swineherd, Eumaeus, who was loyal to him still.

Odysseus went to Eumaeus's hut, and said he was a wandering Cretan soldier. The old man gave him food and warm clothes, and warned him not to go into town, where Penelope's

Odysseus's old dog recognised him despite his disguise.

riotous suitors were killing strangers. Nobody was safe while Prince Telemachus was away seeking his lost father.

Telemachus was in Sparta. Menelaus told him Odysseus was last heard of on Calypso's island. Then Athene came to take him home.

Eumaeus heard footsteps outside his hut, Since his dogs did not bark, he knew it was a friend. It was Telemachus, who sent him to tell Penelope he was back, while he talked to the swineherd's guest. Once they were alone, Athene changed Odysseus into his own shape. The young prince knew his father and wept with joy. They made a plan, and Telemachus returned to the palace.

Next day, Odysseus went to the palace, in his beggar's rags. An old dog sleeping in the courtyard lifted its head as he passed, sniffed, then eagerly jumped up and licked his hand. It was Odysseus's old dog Argos. As he stroked it, it dropped dead from joy.

As Odysseus entered the hall, the drunken suitors greeted the beggar with insults and laughter. Odysseus stayed calm. Penelope sent an old servant to wash the newcomer's feet, as the rules of hospitality required. It was Odysseus's old nurse; she knew him at once, but he signalled to her to keep quiet.

That night, the suitors learned how Penelope had deceived them, and threatened to kill Telemachus unless she chose one of them next day. The desperate queen found a new way to delay. She brought out Odysseus's old bow, which only he could use, and said she would marry the first man who could shoot with it.

Each suitor tried, but none could bend the bow. The last man left to try was the ragged old beggar. All the suitors laughed, but he bent the bow and shot perfectly first time. All were silent. In an instant, Athene turned him back into a king.

Telemachus drew his sword and Odysseus took more arrows. Soon all the suitors lay dead.

Odysseus bent the bow and shot perfectly first time.

About 2000 BC settlers from the north-east began to spread over the mainland and islands of Greece. They spoke a form of Greek, as we know from deciphering their writing, known as Linear B and found on clay tablets. The way of life they brought with them is known as the Mycenaean culture, after the greatest of their settlements, Mycenae.

The Mycenaeans

The Mycenaeans were great seafarers, who founded many colonies around the Aegean Sea and in Cyprus. Their settlements centred on heavily fortified citadels, where the local chief's palace, the homes of his leading warriors, and temples dedicated to different gods, were surrounded by high, thick walls of stone. Such a citadel was known as an acropolis, or 'high city'. On nearby hills were smaller farming villages. The warrior chiefs in the citadel protected the farmers from attack; the farmers supplied the warriors with food.

The Cretans

Another culture existed alongside the Mycenaean one at this time, on the large island of Crete. Crete was far more fertile than mainland Greece, and the farmers there were able to support a multitude of officials, priests, craftsmen and traders, as well as their kings. They could also export some of their produce – wine and raisins, olives and olive oil – to Egypt and other lands. Crete was a rich country, with a civilisation based on large palaces, of which the greatest was Knossos – perhaps the 'original' of Minos's labyrinth, because of its complicated layout. Despite the later legends which show Minos worshipping the Greek gods, the Cretans worshipped a Mother Goddess at small shrines rather than temples.

As islanders, the Cretans had no fear of land-based invaders, and did not need to fortify their palaces. Their wealth was protected by their fleet. But around 1450 BC, the Mycenaeans' sea-power proved too much for them.

An ancient statue of the blind poet Homer. Seven Greek cities claimed to have been his birth place, but no one knows where he was born.

Mycenaean invaders overran the island, and burnt down all the towns and palaces except Knossos, which they may have spared for their own leaders' use. The legend of Theseus and the Minotaur preserves the memory of the conquest of Crete.

Troy

Another of the Mycenaeans' conquests was Troy, a city on a hill in Asia Minor (modern Turkey). The Trojan War took place around 1225 BC. The story has come down to modern times through the writings of Homer, for whom it was already legend. In the 1870s, a German archaeologist called Heinrich Schliemann set out to look for the site of Troy. He found not one city, but nine, buried on top of each other.

The conquest of Troy was perhaps the summit of Mycenaean power. Another wave of invaders, the Dorians, came from the north and took over. But they kept many of the earlier religious practices and legends. Much of what we know of Greek legends comes from writers of the Dorian period, such as Homer and Hesiod.

Homer

The tales we know of the Trojan War and the wanderings of Odysseus come chiefly from two long poems, the *Iliad* and the *Odyssey*, which were probably composed in the eighth century BC. They are said to have been the work of one man, Homer. Legend says that he was a wandering poet, who travelled between the courts of Greece to sing his poems for a living. He was also said to be blind, which meant, for the Greeks, that he could see the supernatural world. Nobody knows if he really existed, and some scholars think the poems were composed by more than one person.

However, the poems were certainly known all over Greece. The *Iliad* has 28 books, which tell only a small part of the whole story of the Trojan War. But for millions of people ever since, this part is the most important. The tale of Odysseus is in 23 books, and is known all over the world. Besides their value as literature, the two poems contain a wealth of information about everyday life, customs and beliefs in ancient Greece.

Greek religion

To the Greeks, nature was a living force, and trees, rocks, streams and all the other things of the natural world were inhabited by living spirits. These spirits, often shown as nymphs, beautiful young women, were god-like, but they could die like humans. When a tree was cut down, the nymph within it died. Other beings, such as the satyrs, with their human bodies and goats' legs, represented the wilder forces of nature. Their leader, the god Pan, could be terrifying. Humans who saw him might suffer the sudden fear we still call 'panic'.

Higher up the scale were the twelve great gods known as the Olympians (see pages 22-23), whom all the Greeks believed in. They, too, were often associated with the forces of nature.

Their king, Zeus, was armed with thunderbolts, and the Greeks saw storms as the effect of his rage. When his brother Poseidon was angry, he beat the sea-bed with his trident and caused earthquakes. The sun's movement during the day was Apollo's chariot crossing the sky. Other gods and goddesses took care of particular human activities: Artemis was the goddess of hunting, Asclepios (Aesculapius) of medicine, Hephaistos of metalsmiths, and Hermes of thieves and merchants.

Myths and reality

Though all the Greeks shared these basic beliefs, there were many local customs and beliefs in different places. Zeus was worshipped in Corinth, in Argos and in Thebes; but different stories were told about him in each city.

The Parthenon was the great temple to Athene on the Acropolis at Athens.

As a result, the same story can be found in different forms in different parts of Greece. Often a local hero (Theseus is an example) is the link between a series of incidents. The story of the twelve labours of Heracles makes one hero responsible for incredible feats carried out in widely separated parts of Greece, whereas the story of the warriors born from dragon's teeth is told about more than one hero. Some myths grew up to say why a city was built in a particular place, or explain something puzzling, such as fossilised dinosaur-bones, which were said to be the bones of giants killed in battle.

Right: *The temple at Delphi drew pilgrims from all over the Mediterranean world.*

Above and right: *Greek artists painted scenes from their mythology on vases – one of the ways in which we know about their legends.*

Greek words

Many words in modern English come from the Greek language. Often, though not always, they are the names inventors gave their new inventions. Often two Greek words are combined to make a new word, and sometimes the word is then shortened: the cinema was originally called the *cinematograph*, and we often shorten *photograph* to *photo*.

English word: *Greek words*

Astronaut: *astron* (star), *nautes* (sailor)
Automatic: *autos* (self); *automatos* (self-moving)
Bible: *biblia* (books)
Biology: *bios* (life), *logos* (word, reason)

Chrysanthemum: *chrysos* (gold), *anthemon* (flower)
Cinema: *kinema* (movement)
Crystal: *krystallos* (ice)
Dinosaur: *deinos* (terrible), *sauros* (lizard)
Electricity: *elektron* (amber)
Graffiti: *graphein* (to write)
Monarch: *monos* (single, alone), *achein* (to rule)
Petroleum: *petra* (rock), *oleum* (oil)
Photograph: *photos* (light), *graphein* (to write)
Planet: *planetes* (wanderer)
Politics: *politikos* (from *polites*, citizen)
Polygon: *polys* (many), *gonia* (angle)
Telephone: *tele* (far), *phone* (sound)

Local differences apart, the Greeks had a single civilisation. Most important of all, they shared a language. Travelling poets brought the greatest stories of Greece to the country's scattered communities, and to the colonies established in other parts of the Mediterranean area.

The oracle

There were places and events which brought members of these communities together, too. Pilgrims came from every part of Greece to consult the oracle at Apollo's great temple of Delphi about problems or to find out about the future. His priestess fell into a trance and spoke a message from the god. But the messages often carried more than one meaning! King Croesus was told that if he went to war, a great empire would fall. Encouraged by this, he attacked the Persian empire of Cyrus.

Athenian coins of the fifth century BC show Athene (below) and her symbol, the owl (right).

This bronze statue of the sea-god Poseidon is in the National Museum at Athens.

But he was shamefully defeated – the empire which fell was his own.

The Olympic Games

The Olympic Games also drew people from all over the Greek world. Every four years, all wars and disputes between cities were stopped for the games, which were held at Zeus's sanctuary at Delphi. Only men could compete or watch. The events included races, on foot and in chariots; discus- and javelin-throwing; jumping; wrestling and boxing. The overall winner received a crown of laurel-leaves, and a poem was recited in his honour.

The greatest years of Greek civilisation were the fifth and sixth centuries BC. But its poetry, drama, philosophy and art have influenced people ever since. The myths and legends of Greece are among the glories of European civilisation.

INDEX